I'm mixed!

MAGGY WILLIAMS

ILLUSTRATED BY ELIZABETH HASEGAWA AGRESTA

Loving Healing Press

Ann Arbor

Distributed by Ingram Book Group (USA/CAN/AU), Bertrams Books (UK/EU)

ISBN 978-1-61599-359-8 paperback
ISBN 978-1-61599-360-4 hardcover
ISBN 978-1-61599-361-1 eBook (PDF, ePub, Kindle)

Published by
Loving Healing Press
5145 Pontiac Trail
Ann Arbor, MI 48105

Toll free: 888-761-6268 (USA/CAN)
Fax: 734-663-6861

www.LHPress.com
info@LHPress.com

Distributed by Ingram Book Group (USA/CAN), Bertram's Books (UK/EU)

Cover Background Illustration: D.E. West / ZAQ Designs

Author's Note

Dear Reader,

Whether you are black or brown or white or tan, you are beautiful and you deserve to be loved.

As for me, I've always had skin the color of honey. I got it because my mom is white and my dad is black. I didn't know my dad. My mom raised me all by herself. And I was really lucky because she taught me that I wasn't just black or just white. I was both.

I used to love to read. From the minute I learned how to do it, I'd stay up late, under the covers, with my secret flashlight, reading so late that the next day I'd fall asleep in my cereal. I read and read and read. And I found books with white main characters, or black, or Hispanic, or Asian, but none about kids who were lucky enough to be mixed—like me.

So I made a promise to my little girl self that, when I grew up, I would write a book that helped kids like me celebrate all sides of themselves. This is that book.

Love,
Maggy Williams

I will not say that I'm just black,

that might make my
mom feel bad.

I will not say that I'm just white,

'cause that leaves out
my dad.

Instead, I am proud of
the shape of my nose,

of all of my features
from my head to my
toes.

Of my smooth honey skin and my soft curly hair.

And I don't even mind if
some people stare.

And when they ask me, "Are you black or white?"

I say, "I'm mixed."

And that suits them all right.

They say "You are beautiful!" And I smile with glee!

I know I'm accepted for just being me.

For never pretending to be just one race or another,

for never forgetting my
father or mother.

I raise my head up to the sky and cry to all I see,

"I'm black, I'm white,
I'm beautiful,
I'm mixed, and I'm
proud to be me!"

About the Author – Maggy Williams

Maggy Williams started writing at five years old and hasn't stopped since. She loves creating stories for young readers because they have the best imaginations and because she never wants to grow up. When she's not writing, she enjoys acting and comedy improv, which is basically just make-believe for grown-ups.

About the Artist – Elizabeth Hasegawa Agresta

Originally from Vancouver, Elizabeth is a third-generation artist who moved to Connecticut in 1989. Elizabeth studied at the Silvermine School of Art, and today is best known for her urban and landscape paintings. With three mixed children of their own, she and her husband, Thomas, especially appreciate the timeliness and optimism of Maggy's work.

As a biracial child, Maggy Williams had three options. She could identify as black, white, or mixed. She chose to embrace her multiracial heritage because she was taught that she could. Her hope is that this book will help children realize it is possible to integrate their multiple racial identities.

Lightning Source UK Ltd.
Milton Keynes UK
UKRC032019230922
409363UK00004B/123